Zinc ALLOY

VS

FRANKENSTEIN

 Raintree

R www.raintreepublishers.co.uk
Visit our website to find out
more information about
Raintree books.

To order:
☎ Phone 0845 6044371
🖩 Fax +44 (0) 1865 312263
📧 Email myorders@raintreepublishers.co.uk

Customers from outside the UK please telephone +44 1865 312262

Raintree is an imprint of Capstone Global Library Limited, a company incorporated
in England and Wales having its registered office at 7 Pilgrim Street, London,
EC4V 6LB – Registered company number: 6695582

Text © Stone Arch Books 2009
First published in hardback and paperback in the United Kingdom
by Capstone Global Library in 2010
The moral rights of the proprietor have been asserted.

Designer: Brann Garvey
Series Editor: Donald Lemke
Associate Editor: Sean Tulien
Art Director: Bob Lentz
Creative Director: Heather Hindseth
Editorial Director: Michael Dahl
Editor: Vaarunika Dharmapala
Originated by Capstone Global Library Ltd
Printed and bound in China by Leo Paper Products Ltd

ISBN 978 1 406216 51 6 (hardback)
14 13 12 11 10
10 9 8 7 6 5 4 3 2 1

ISBN 978 1 406216 74 5 (paperback)
14 13 12 11 10
10 9 8 7 6 5 4 3 2 1

British Library Cataloguing in Publication Data
A full catalogue record for this book is available from the British Library.

Zinc ALLOY

vs

FRANKENSTEIN

by Donald Lemke   illustrated by Douglas Holgate

8

18

About the author

Donald Lemke is a children's book editor. He is the author of the Zinc Alloy graphic novel adventure series. He also wrote *Captured Off Guard*, a World War II story, and a graphic novelization of *Gulliver's Travels*, both of which were selected by the American Junior Library Guild.

About the illustrator

Douglas Holgate is a freelance illustrator from Melbourne, Australia. His work has been published all around the world by Random House, Simon and Schuster, the *New Yorker* magazine, and Image Comics. His award-winning comic "Laika" appears in the acclaimed comic collection *Flight, Volume Two*.

Glossary

angry mob large group of people using force to get what they want

cower hide in fear or shame

heroic very brave or daring

force power behind the movement of something

innocent not guilty, or undeserving of punishment

legend a story from long ago

miniature smaller than the usual size

reverse change to the opposite position or path

rotating turning around like a wheel

thruster object that causes forward or upward force

More about Frankenstein

The original novel about Frankenstein was published in 1818 by Mary Shelley. She wrote it when she was just 19 years old!

Shelley's name didn't appear on the first edition of *Frankenstein*. It wasn't on the novel until the second edition was printed in 1823.

In Mary Shelley's novel, the monster was not called Frankenstein. In fact, Shelley never named the monster.

In the novel, Doctor Victor Frankenstein is the mad scientist who gives the monster life. Some historians believe that Shelley based her mad scientist on a real-life physician, Johann Konrad Dippel of Germany.

Dippel was born and continued to live in Castle Frankenstein in Germany until his death in 1734. An annual Halloween party is now held at what remains of the 800-year-old castle.

The first film about the monster Frankenstein was 12 minutes long. It was shown in 1910. Like other films during this time, it didn't have any sound.

The modern version of Frankenstein comes from the 1931 *Frankenstein* film. Many sequels have stemmed from it, including *Bride of Frankenstein*, *Son of Frankenstein*, and *Ghost of Frankenstein*.

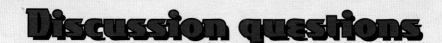

Discussion questions

1. Zinc Alloy was trying to help, but his plan didn't work. Was it fair for the entire town to turn against him?

2. Zinc Alloy and Frankenstein are really just normal kids who dress up. If you could be any superhero, who would you be and why?

3. Both Zack and Frankie were bullied at school. Have you ever been bullied? How did that make you feel?

Writing prompts

1. Zinc and Frankenstein both like the same comic book. What do you and your friends have in common? Make a list of at least 10 things that you and your friends like.

2. Zack used an on-the-go travel suit to turn into Zinc Alloy. Invent another way for Zack to turn into Zinc. Be sure to name and describe your new invention.

3. Write a newspaper article about how Zinc Alloy and Frankenstein cleaned up the town. Be sure to include some quotes from townspeople.

More amazing adventures!

Meet Tiger Moth, the insect ninja who takes on some of the world's baddest bugs with his faithful friend Kung Pow. But that's nothing compared to tackling the times tables...